The HOME is BEST Book

by KATHLEEN N. DALY

Pictures by JAN PFLOOG
formerly THE NEST BOOK

 GOLDEN PRESS
Western Publishing Company, Inc.
Racine, Wisconsin

© MCMLXVIII, MCMLXXVI by Western Publishing Company, Inc.
All rights reserved. Produced in U.S.A.

GOLDEN®, A GOLDEN SHAPE BOOK®, and GOLDEN PRESS®
are trademarks of Western Publishing Company, Inc. No part
of this book may be reproduced or copied in any form without
written permission from the publisher.

Fourth Printing, 1979

East, West, home is best—
sometimes home's a hanging nest.

A cave is home to big, black Bear.

A cozy den is Fox's lair.

Goldfish lives in a see-through bowl.

Mousie lives in a deep, warm hole.

Seal finds it very nice . . . .

... swimming under northern ice.

The barn is home to gentle Cow.

Squirrel lives high up on a bough.

Dog's at home in his own snug house.

Martins have an apartment house.

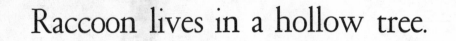

Raccoon lives in a hollow tree.

And Pussycat lives here—with me.